THE CAT'S

also by Norman Thelwell

Angels on Horseback
Thelwell Country
Thelwell in Orbit
A Place of Your Own
A Leg at Each Corner
Thelwell's Riding Academy
Top Dog
Up the Garden Path
Compleat Tangler
Thelwell's Book of Leisure
This Desirable Plot
The Effluent Society
Thelwell's Magnificat
Penelope
Three Sheets in the Wind
Belt Up
Thelwell Goes West
Thelwell's Brat Race
Thelwell's Gymkhana
A Plank Bridge by a Pool
A Millstone Round My Neck
Thelwell's Pony Cavalcade
Some Damn Fool's Signed the Rubens Again
Thelwell's Sporting Prints
Wrestling with a Pencil
Play It as It Lies
Thelwell's Pony Panorama
Penelope Rides Again

thelwell

THE CAT'S PYJAMAS

Mandarin

A Mandarin Humour Paperback

THE CAT'S PYJAMAS

First published in Great Britain in 1992
by Methuen London
First published in paperback in 1993
by Mandarin Paperbacks
an imprint of Reed Consumer Books Ltd
Michelin House, 81 Fulham Road, London SW3 6RB
and Auckland, Melbourne, Singapore and Toronto

Copyright © 1992 by Norman Thelwell
The author has asserted his moral rights

A CIP catalogue record for this book
is available from the British Library
ISBN 0 7493 1346 3

Printed and bound in Great Britain
by Cox & Wyman Ltd, Reading, Berkshire

CONTENTS

MIXED MOGGIES

Hep cat

Greedy cat

Alley cat

Copy cat

Scaredy cat

Wild cat

Cool cat

Silly cat

Lucky cat

Our cat

Your cat

Top cat

Hell cat

Marmalade cat

FELINE PHRASES

Cat's cradle

Cat's-paw

The cat's whiskers

Cat-ice

Cat burglar

Catmint

Cataract

Cat-o'-nine-tails

Catlick

Cat litter

Catcall

Catnap

Catnip

Cat lap

Catwalk

Catfish

CAT A LYST

Catkin

Catsup

Caterwaul

Catapult

Catgut

Catoptrics

Catastrophe

Catarrh

Catacomb

Catacoustics

Catacaustic

Catechu

Caterpillar

Catatonic

Catafalque

TOMFOOLERY

Tom Thumb

Tom-tom

Tombola

Tomahawk

Tomato

Kittiwake

Kitbag

Pussyfoot

Pussy willow

Puss moths

Glamour puss

Sourpuss

Polypus

Campus

Metacarpus

Platypus

Octopus

Opus

Habeas corpus

A CAT CAN LOOK
AT A KING

No room to swing a cat

Enough to make a cat laugh

Belling the cat

Letting the cat out of the bag

A cat-and-dog life

Cat got your tongue?

See which way the cat jumps

The cat that swallowed the canary

Cat among the pigeons

All black cats are not witches

Old cats mean young mice

*Cats have an uncanny knack
of foretelling earthquakes*

The cat that scratches,
scratches for itself

Whoever cares for a cat
will have a happy marriage

No matter how much cats fight . . .

there always seem to be plenty of kittens

If a girl treads on a cat's tail,
she will not find a husband
for another year

No man can build a door
which is proof against a cat or a lover

*A sneezing cat
is a sure sign of rain*

It is unlucky to cross a stream
when carrying a cat

Cats know how to
obtain food without labour . . .

shelter without confinement . . .

. . . and love without penalty